Happy Birthday

Jan Joss
illustrated by Bruce Day

© 1998 Journey Books
   Published by Bob Jones University Press
   Greenville, SC 29614
   ISBN 0-89084-979-X

Ted handed a bag to Deb.

2

"It is for you, Deb."

3

"Happy birthday!"

Pat handed
a bag to Deb.

"It is for you, Deb."

6

"Happy birthday!

Happy birthday, Debbie.

It is for you!"

7

Can a hand sand?

band	banded
hand	handed
sand	sanded

Service words:

for you

Enrichment words:

birthday dear happy